20TH CENTURY SCIENCE & TECHNOLOGY

1970–90

COMPUTERS AND CHIPS

20TH CENTURY SCIENCE & TECHNOLOGY – 1970-90
was produced by

David West Children's Books
7 Princeton Court
55 Felsham Road
London SW15 1AZ

Designers: Jenny Skelly & Aarti Parmar
Editor: James Pickering
Picture Research: Brooks Krikler Research

First published in Great Britain in 2000 by
Heinemann Library, Halley Court, Jordan Hill, Oxford OX2 8EJ, a division of Reed Educational and Professional Publishing Limited.

OXFORD MELBOURNE AUCKLAND
JOHANNESBURG BLANTYRE GABORONE
IBADAN PORTSMOUTH (NH) USA CHICAGO

04 03 02 01 00
10 9 8 7 6 5 4 3 2 1

ISBN 0 431 12194 X (HB)
ISBN 0 431 12201 6 (PB)

British Library Cataloguing in Publication Data

Parker, Steve, 1952 -
1970 - 1990 computers and chips.-
(Twentieth century science & technology).
1. Technology - History - 20th century -
Juvenile literature
2. Science - History - 20th century -
Juvenile literature
3. Space stations - Juvenile literature
I. Title
609' .047

Printed and bound in Italy

PHOTO CREDITS :
Abbreviations: t-top, m-middle, b-bottom, r-right, l-left, c-centre.

Cover m & pages 18t & 29tl - Solution Pictures. Cover b & Pages 4-5 & 22-23 - Apple Macintosh. 4, 11tl & tr, 14 both, 15 & 27bl & br - Corbis Images. 5t - JVC. 5m, 8 all, 9, 10 all, 11ml, mr & bl, 12 all, 13, 17t & 23m - NASA. 6t, 16t, 16-17, 21b, 23b, 25b, 26r & 27t - Frank Spooner Pictures. 6b - Oxford Scientific Films. 7, 16b, 17b, 19 both, 20-21, 24-25, 26l, 28 both & 29tr - Rex Features. 11br - European Space Agency. 18m - British Aerospace Airbus. 21t - Sandia. 24t - British Airways. 24b - Peugeot. 25t - Sinclair.

The dates in brackets after a person's name give the years that he or she lived.

An explanation of difficult words can be found in the glossary on page 30.

20TH CENTURY SCIENCE & TECHNOLOGY

1970-90

COMPUTERS AND CHIPS

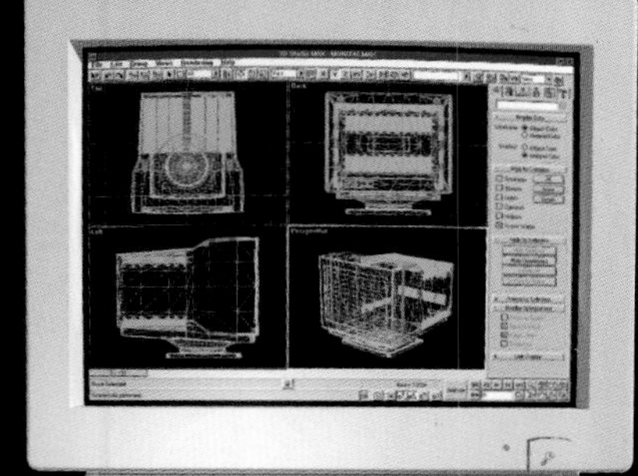

Steve Parker

Heinemann
LIBRARY

CONTENTS

The space shuttle, a new kind of spacecraft that could be used many times, first blasted off in 1981. However, in 1986 a disaster set the shuttle programme back many years.

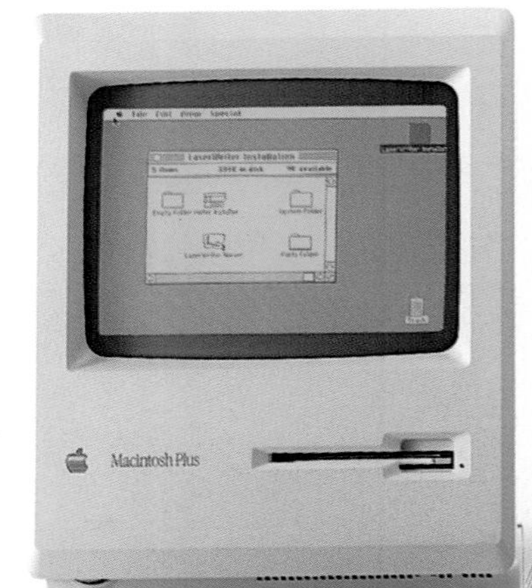

Apple computers like the early Macintosh pioneered easy-to-use on-screen lists, or menus, of various options.

TWO SIDES OF SCIENCE

The 1960s had been a great success for science and technology, ending with the first Moon landing in 1969. During the 1970s progress continued even faster, especially in electronics and computing. In the 1980s, personal computers became more widespread, although they were still mainly used for work rather than leisure and entertainment. However there was a negative side too. Disasters occurred and problems appeared. Pollution became world news with oil slicks washed on to the coast, smog over cities, leaks from chemical factories and nuclear power stations, acid rain, the 'ozone hole' and early evidence for global warming. These problems were not because of science itself, but the way science was being used or applied. People joined campaigns to increase safety, protect the environment and conserve natural resources. Science and technology needed more control.

The 1980s saw the spread of hand-held video cameras, allowing people to make 'home videos'.

In 1975 astronauts from the rival superpowers, USSR and USA, shook hands in space.

The USSR's Mir *space station was launched in 1986 and finally abandoned in 1999.*

1970–90 STRANGE IDEAS

Scientists devised many strange ideas and explored many remote places during the 1970s, from the farthest reaches of outer space to the bottom of the sea here on Earth.

In 1986 the submersible *Alvin* explored the wreck of the ocean liner *Titanic*, which sank in the north-west Atlantic in 1912.

INNER SPACE

The three-person deep-sea craft *Alvin*, launched in 1964, made exciting discoveries. In 1977 it found unexpected life on the deep sea bed in the eastern Pacific Ocean. Giant worms as thick as a human arm, shellfish the size of dining plates, blind crabs and creeping fish clustered around cracks in the ocean floor where hot, dark, mineral-rich water spurted out from far below.

NEW LIFE

These eerie deep-sea creatures were entirely new to science. How do they survive in the cold blackness? Microbes, especially bacteria, in their bodies take in the energy-rich minerals from the water. They use the minerals for growth and, in turn, supply energy and nutrients for the animals to use. The ocean floor cracks are known as deep-sea hydrothermal vents. The animals around them were the first creatures to be discovered on Earth which do not depend on the Sun. On land and in shallow seas animals eat plants, or eat other animals which have eaten plants – and plants need sunlight to grow. This discovery raised the possibility of life on other worlds powered by the energy in minerals rather than light from a star.

Huge worms and ghostly crabs crowd around a 'black smoker' – a dark plume of mineral-rich water flowing through a crack or vent in the deep sea bed.

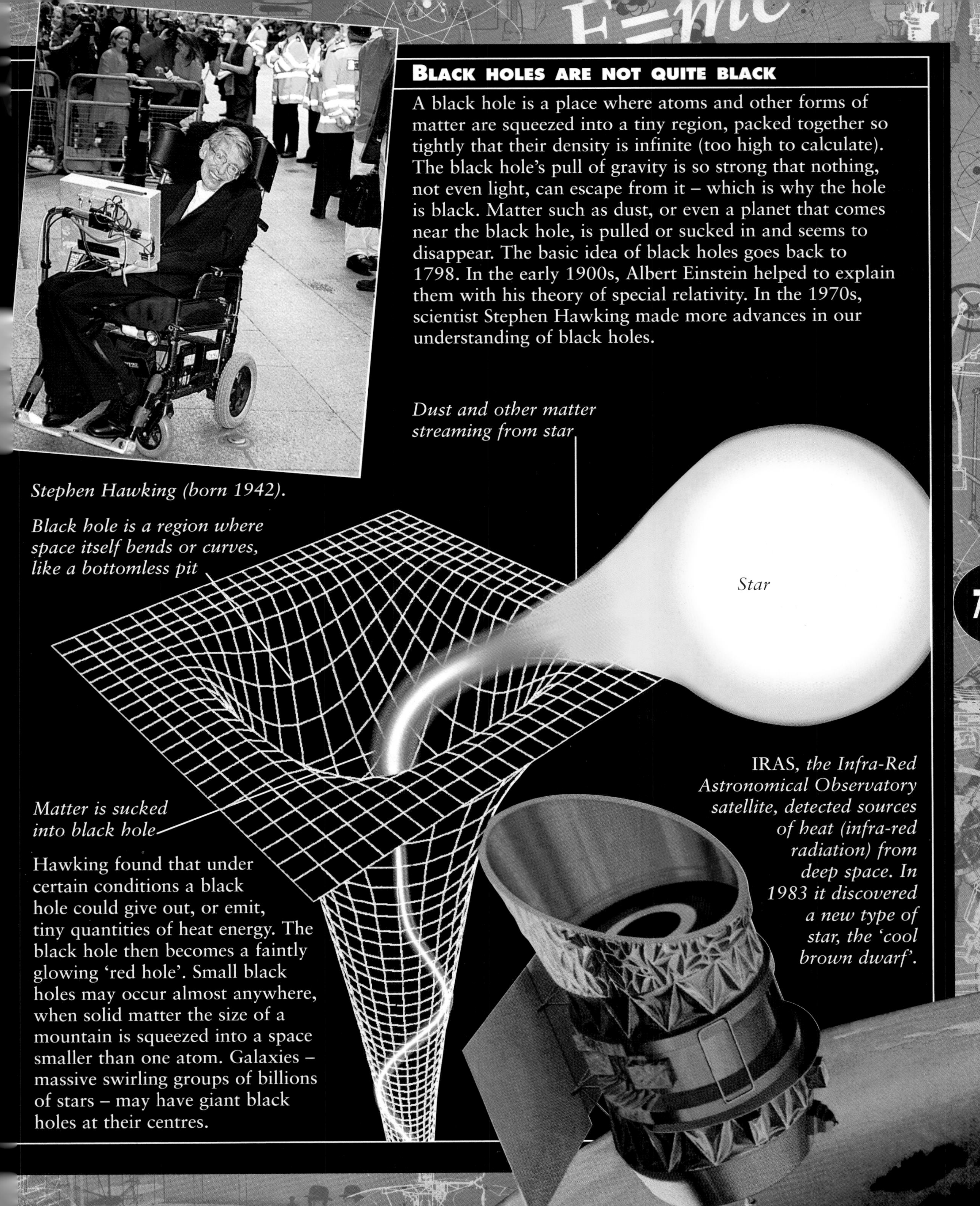

Stephen Hawking (born 1942).

IRAS, *the Infra-Red Astronomical Observatory satellite, detected sources of heat (infra-red radiation) from deep space. In 1983 it discovered a new type of star, the 'cool brown dwarf'.*

Black holes are not quite black

A black hole is a place where atoms and other forms of matter are squeezed into a tiny region, packed together so tightly that their density is infinite (too high to calculate). The black hole's pull of gravity is so strong that nothing, not even light, can escape from it – which is why the hole is black. Matter such as dust, or even a planet that comes near the black hole, is pulled or sucked in and seems to disappear. The basic idea of black holes goes back to 1798. In the early 1900s, Albert Einstein helped to explain them with his theory of special relativity. In the 1970s, scientist Stephen Hawking made more advances in our understanding of black holes.

Hawking found that under certain conditions a black hole could give out, or emit, tiny quantities of heat energy. The black hole then becomes a faintly glowing 'red hole'. Small black holes may occur almost anywhere, when solid matter the size of a mountain is squeezed into a space smaller than one atom. Galaxies – massive swirling groups of billions of stars – may have giant black holes at their centres.

OBSERVING EARTH

After the excitement of the Moon landings in the 1960s, the 1970s became the decade of satellite launches. Dozens of research, weather and survey satellites were put into orbit, to look down on Earth and also out into space.

Seasat *(Specialized Experimental Applications Satellite) was 12 m long and launched in June 1978.*

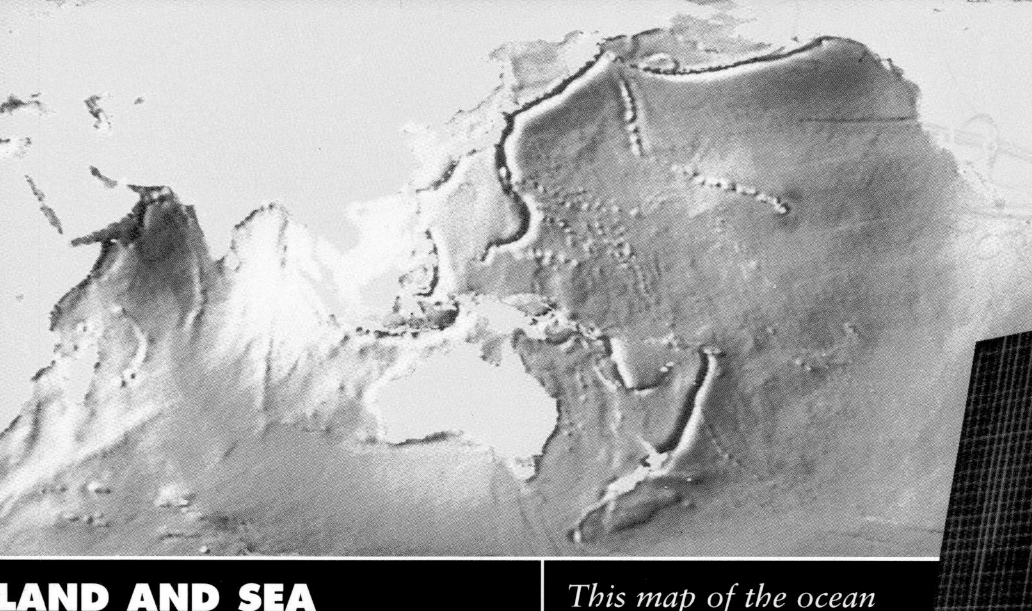

This map of the ocean floor, showing deep-sea trenches, was made using information from Seasat.

LAND AND SEA

From 1972 the series of Landsat satellites was put into specialized orbits (see opposite) by the USA. They carried a range of cameras, not only for ordinary light photographs, but also for images of heat and other types of energy given off by the Earth. Their detailed photographs are used in many ways – by farmers studying crop fields, foresters planning new woodlands, environmental experts looking at habitat destruction and geologists searching for oil, coal and other resources. For four months in 1978 another satellite, *Seasat*, provided precise information about the oceans, their temperatures, wind speeds, currents and even wave heights.

Landsa
launched 19

WHAT'S THE WEATHER?

Meteorological satellites such as *Nimbus* and *Meteosat* carried cameras to photograph clouds, storms and other weather features. Each *Nimbus* was about three metres long and weighed up to one tonne. It took about 1,500 pictures every day. The satellite's sensors detected temperature, humidity, wind speed and similar conditions. Their vast amounts of information helped forecasters to predict the weather and also showed how the global climate may be changing because of the greenhouse effect. *Nimbus 3* was launched in 1970. The last of the series, *Nimbus 7*, went into orbit in 1978. It was the first satellite designed to detect polluting chemicals in the atmosphere.

Drum surface covered with solar cells to change sunlight into electricity

Meteosat 1 *was launched in 1974 and* Meteosat 2 *in '75. Each was a drum shape measuring 1.9 m across, 3.4 m in total length and 245 kg in weight. They were put into geosynchronous orbit, that is, one orbit every 24 hours. Seen from Earth, they stayed in the same place in the sky.*

SPECIAL ORBITS

Satellites have different orbits around Earth depending on their jobs. Landsats have low polar orbits. They travel over the North and South Poles, taking 'strips' of images as the Earth spins once each day beneath. At their closest they are less than 900 km above the surface, so their cameras can 'see' amazing detail. Landsats and similar satellites are also used by the military to check on the movements of warships, fighter planes, tanks and even marching ranks of soldiers.

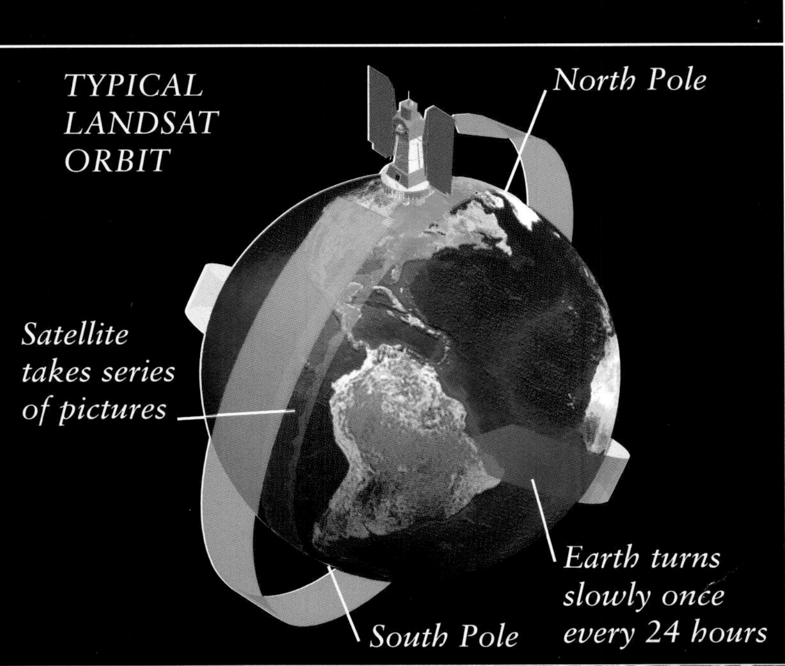

EXPLORING SPACE

A series of unmanned deep-space probes launched in the 1970s-80s vastly improved our knowledge of the Sun and its planets.

MERCURY

Mariner 10 *took close-up photos of Mercury and Venus, and discovered Mercury's natural magnetic field.*

WE ARE HERE

The Voyager probes both carried plaques showing the likeness of a man and woman and a map of Earth's position in space. One day an alien intelligence may find the probe and perhaps visit us.

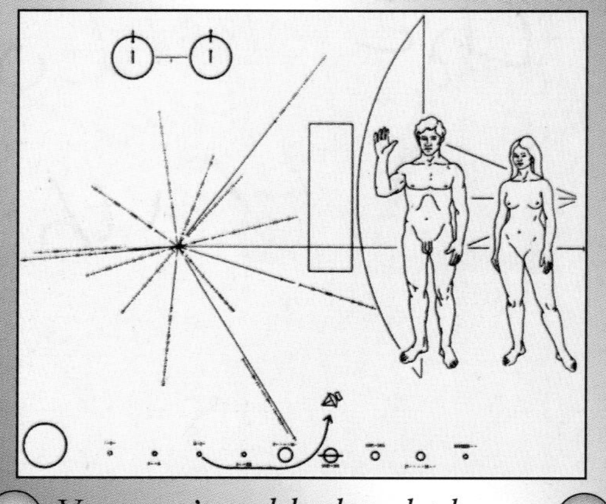

Voyager's gold-plated plaque.

THE INNER PLANETS

Mariner probes were designed to study planets relatively near Earth and close to the Sun – Mercury, Venus and Mars. In 1971 *Mariner 9* travelled to Mars and took many spectacular photographs of its huge mountains and vast valleys. *Mariner 10* was blasted into space in 1973 and passed within 5,770 kilometres of Venus, photographing its dense clouds. Using the planet's pull of gravity as a 'slingshot' the probe rushed onwards to encounter the innermost planet, Mercury, three times. The final pass in March 1975 was just 325 kilometres away.

VENUS

LIFE ON MARS?

In 1975 two US spacecraft, *Vikings 1* and 2, were sent to explore Mars. They arrived in 1976. Each craft separated into two parts. The orbiter went around the planet, taking photographs and sensor readings, while the lander parachuted to a soft touchdown on the surface. The landers also took hundreds of photographs, measured gases in the atmosphere, and scooped up samples of the reddish soil to test for signs of life. There were none.

Orbiter and lander separate

Orbiter receives signals from lander and sends them to Earth

Thrusters position lander for entry into atmosphere

Lander's parachute opens at 6,000 m

Soft landing as sensors on 'feet' shut down engines

Viking *lander*

THE OUTER PLANETS

US probes *Voyager 1* and 2, both launched in 1977, made incredible journeys to the giant planets in the farthest parts of the Solar System. *Voyager 1* passed within 270,000 kilometres of Jupiter, the largest planet, in 1979. The next year it travelled to within 120,000 kilometres of the ringed planet Saturn. *Voyager 2* also flew past Jupiter and Saturn, then approached within 80,000 kilometres of Uranus in 1986. Three years later it encountered the second-farthest planet, Neptune, passing only 5,000 kilometres away. Both *Voyagers* have now left the Solar System and are speeding through interstellar space, carrying pictures on plaques (see opposite).

Each Voyager *had a dish-shaped antenna 3.7 m across, to send and receive radio signals from Earth. The whole craft weighed 815 kg.*

The Giotto *probe, launched in 1985 by a European* Ariane *rocket, passed by Halley's comet in 1986. It discovered that the ice-and-dust core is only 10 km across.*

1970-90

SPACE STATIONS

After short trips into space the next great challenge was to live there for weeks, months, perhaps even years. Could the human body cope with conditions such as weightlessness, lack of exercise and the feeling of isolation?

Skylab *needed a replacement gold 'sunshade' after an accident at launch.*

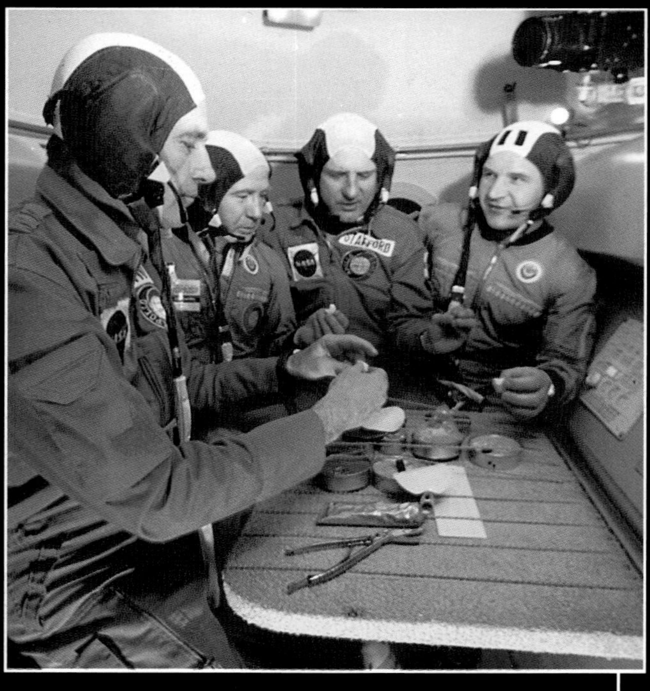

US and USSR astronauts train in a mock-up of the USSR's Soyuz *craft, early 1975.*

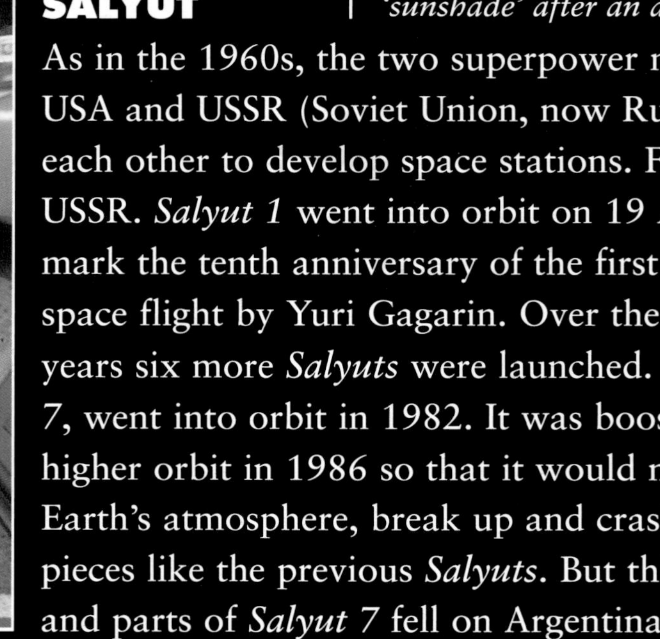

SALYUT

As in the 1960s, the two superpower nations of the USA and USSR (Soviet Union, now Russia/CIS) raced each other to develop space stations. First was the USSR. *Salyut 1* went into orbit on 19 April 1971, to mark the tenth anniversary of the first ever manned space flight by Yuri Gagarin. Over the following years six more *Salyuts* were launched. The last, *Salyut 7*, went into orbit in 1982. It was boosted into a higher orbit in 1986 so that it would not re-enter Earth's atmosphere, break up and crash to Earth in pieces like the previous *Salyuts*. But this did not work and parts of *Salyut 7* fell on Argentina.

SKYLAB

The US *Skylab* space station blasted off in 1973, housed in a modified *Saturn V* rocket casing. Soon after launch one of its two solar panels was torn off, and the other panel and a shield to protect against the Sun's rays were damaged. Four crews visited the station in *Apollo* spacecraft over nine months, carrying our repairs and many scientific experiments.

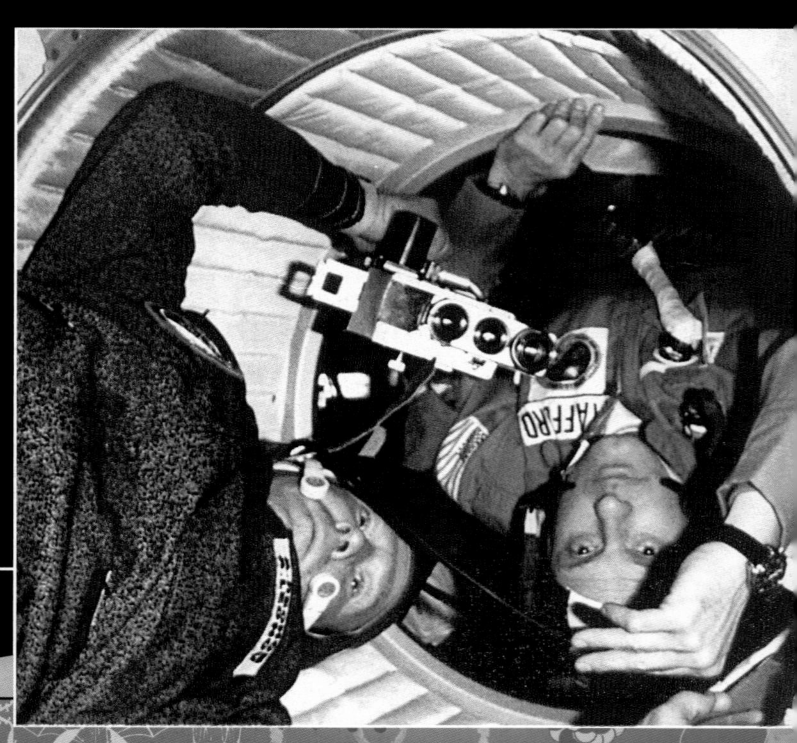

In a symbol of superpower cooperation, astronauts meet as Apollo *and* Soyuz *dock in orbit, July 1975.*

The Salyut space station

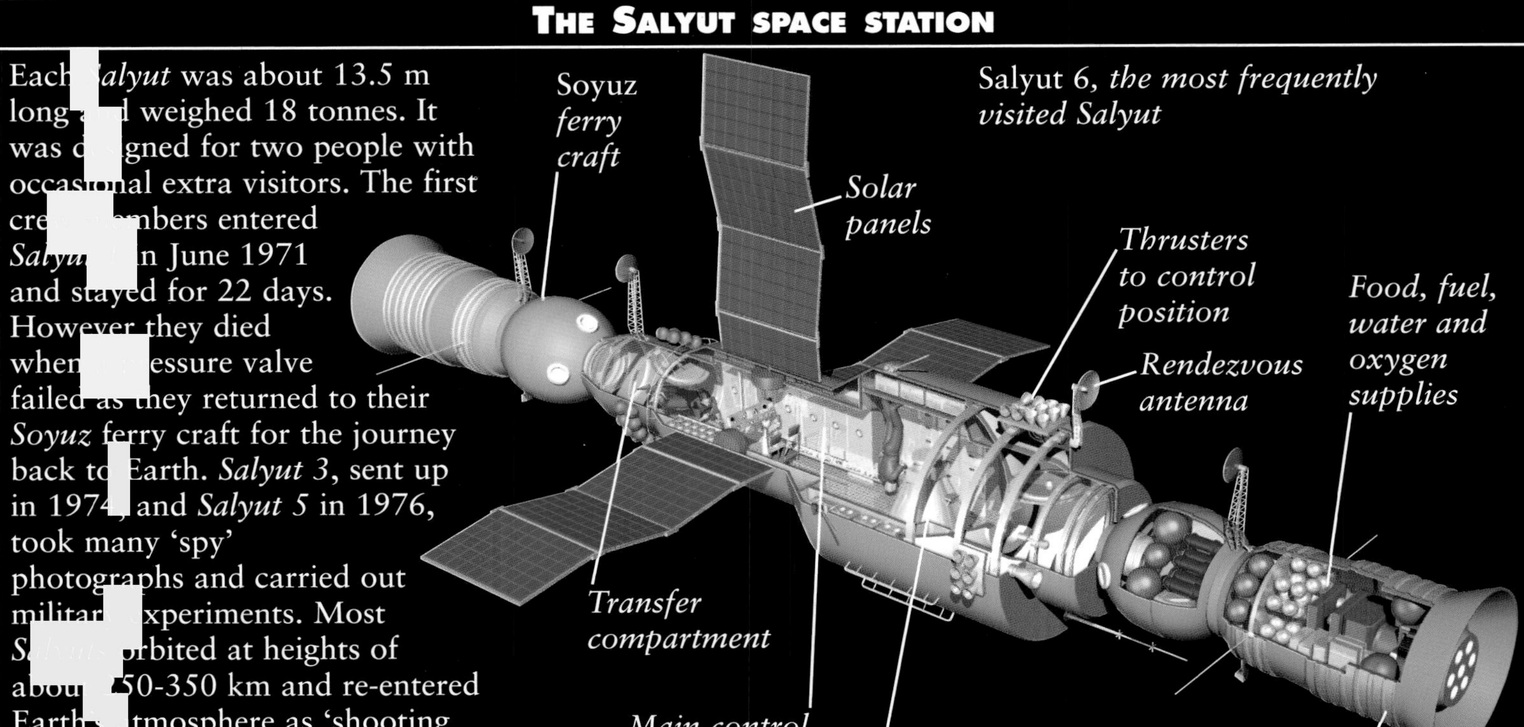

Each *Salyut* was about 13.5 m long and weighed 18 tonnes. It was designed for two people with occasional extra visitors. The first crew members entered *Salyut 1* in June 1971 and stayed for 22 days. However they died when a pressure valve failed as they returned to their *Soyuz* ferry craft for the journey back to Earth. *Salyut 3*, sent up in 1974, and *Salyut 5* in 1976, took many 'spy' photographs and carried out military experiments. Most *Salyuts* orbited at heights of about 250-350 km and re-entered Earth's atmosphere as 'shooting stars' in about one year. *Salyut 7* did not burn up until 1991.

MIR

The USSR's space station *Mir* (Russian for 'peace') was put into orbit in 1986. Its basic structure or core was 17 metres long and four metres wide, larger than *Salyut*. *Mir* also had better facilities including more windows, two private compartments and extra ports or hatches for linking to other craft. Basic supplies were regularly ferried to *Mir* in unmanned *Progress* craft, and scientific equipment and experiments in *Kvant* craft. The astronauts themselves travelled up and down in *Soyuz TM* craft.

In 1988 USSR astronauts Musa Manarov and Vladimir Titov became the first people to spend a year in space, on board Mir. *In this view the station core is vertical with various ferry craft, including* Kvant *and* Soyuz, *attached in the middle.*

1970-90

SPACE SHUTTLE

1981 saw the start of a new era in space. The US space shuttles did not burn up on re-entry or drift away from Earth. They flew back down to Earth, to be used again.

In orbit the doors on the orbiter's payload bay open so that satellites or other objects can be released.

The shuttle blasts off using two solid rocket boosters (SRBs) and an external fuel tank. This is non-reusable and burns up in the atmosphere, while the SRBs parachute back to Earth.

REUSEABLE SPACEPLANE

A space shuttle has four main parts. One is the spaceplane itself, the orbiter. There were originally five orbiters – *Enterprise*, *Columbia*, *Challenger, Atlantis* and *Discovery*. First into space was *Columbia*, between 12 and 14 April 1981. At launch the orbiter's three rocket engines are supplied with liquid oxygen and fuel from a giant fuel tank 47 metres tall. There are also two solid fuel rocket boosters on either side of the tank. The boosters and tank fall away as the orbiter approaches its maximum height.

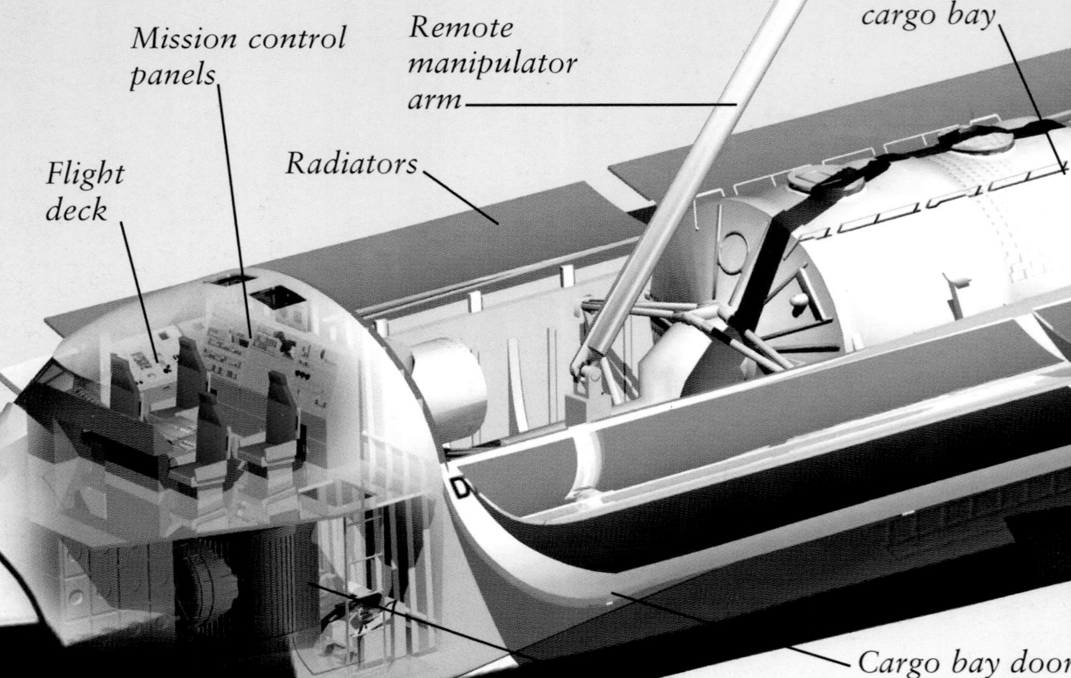

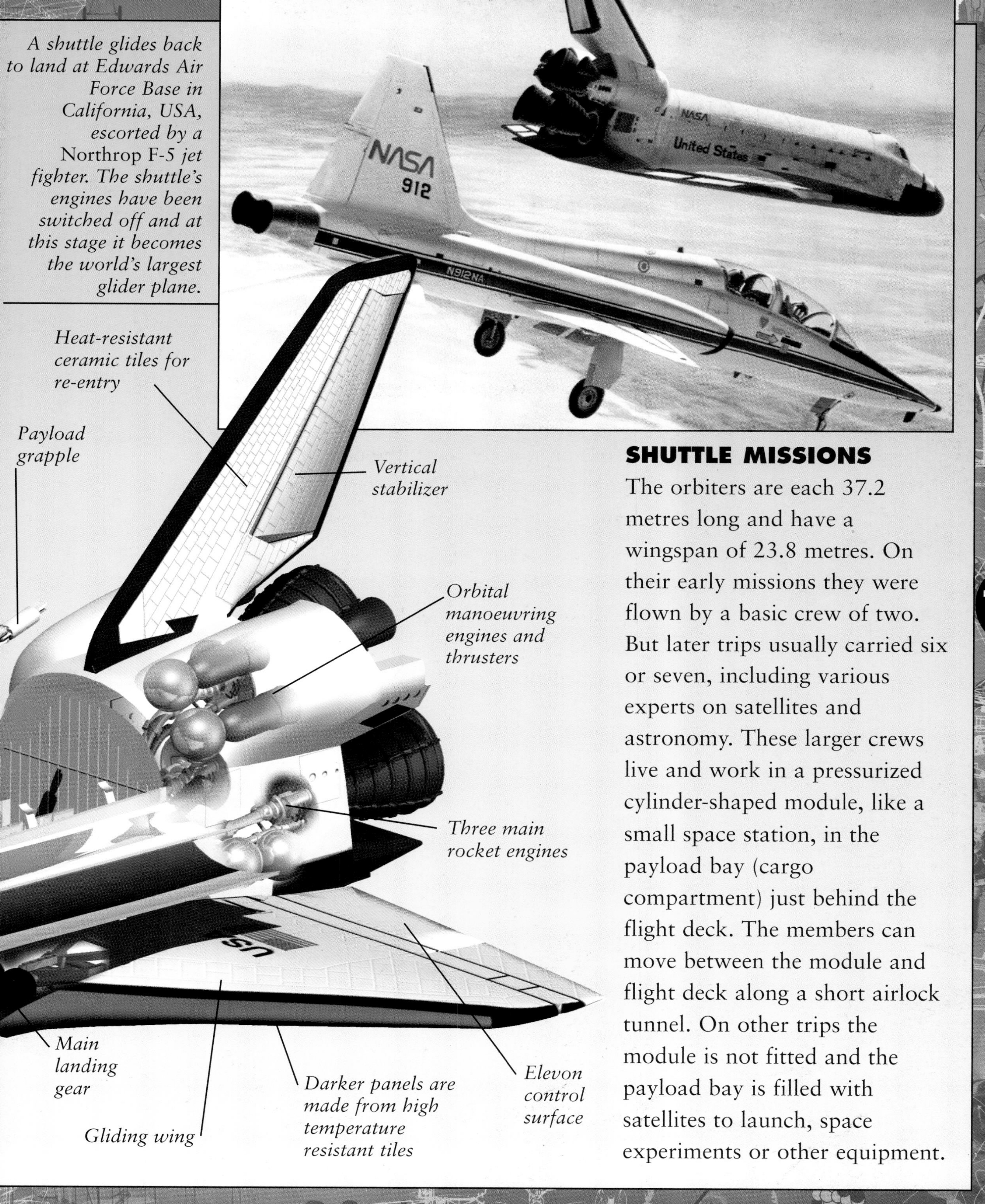

A shuttle glides back to land at Edwards Air Force Base in California, USA, escorted by a Northrop F-5 jet fighter. The shuttle's engines have been switched off and at this stage it becomes the world's largest glider plane.

SHUTTLE MISSIONS

The orbiters are each 37.2 metres long and have a wingspan of 23.8 metres. On their early missions they were flown by a basic crew of two. But later trips usually carried six or seven, including various experts on satellites and astronomy. These larger crews live and work in a pressurized cylinder-shaped module, like a small space station, in the payload bay (cargo compartment) just behind the flight deck. The members can move between the module and flight deck along a short airlock tunnel. On other trips the module is not fitted and the payload bay is filled with satellites to launch, space experiments or other equipment.

1970-90

SCIENCE IN THE DOCK

In 1976, a cloud of poisonous gas accidentally escaped from a chemical factory in Seveso, Italy. It was the first of various science-based disasters.

Many victims of the Bhopal tragedy suffered blindness.

SEVESO

The Seveso cloud contained dioxins, dangerous chemicals which are by-products of making herbicides. They can pollute the soil and harm living things. Farm animals, dogs and other pets died at Seveso, but no people were killed. Even so the accident made many people aware of the problems that science-based processes might cause.

An aerial view of the terrible destruction of the nuclear reactor at Chernobyl.

BHOPAL

In 1984, another leak at a chemical factory released a cloud of gas over the city of Bhopal, India. In this crowded neighbourhood hundreds of people were injured. Questions were asked not only about the safety of the factory itself, but also about the wisdom of siting possibly dangerous factories in built-up areas.

Workers wearing protective suits and masks prepare to clean up the Seveso site in Italy.

NUCLEAR DISASTER

The Chernobyl disaster began with a leak in a cooling pipe near the base of the nuclear core. Water poured out and reacted with the graphite (a form of carbon) which helps to control the nuclear splitting process. The reaction produced hydrogen gas which collected and then exploded.

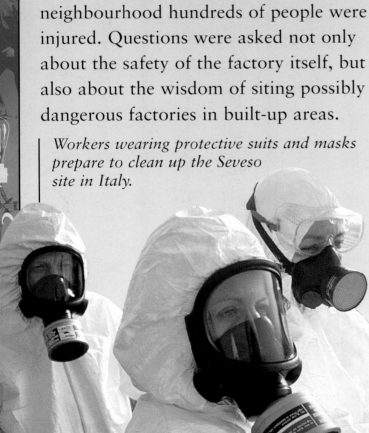

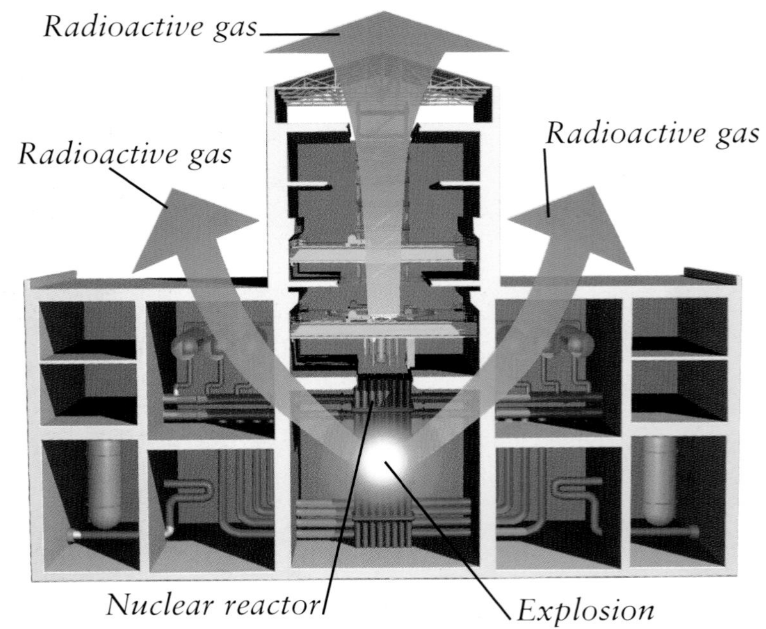

CHERNOBYL

In 1986, a small leak in a water pipe set off a chain of events that caused a terrible tragedy. It led to an explosion in the Number 4 nuclear reactor at the Chernobyl power station near Kiev, Ukraine. The explosion and its aftermath killed 31 people. It also allowed radioactive gas to escape from the huge building, drift away and cause pollution over a vast area including parts of Europe. Soil, farm crops and animals were contaminated for several years.

MORE TRAGEDIES

In the same year, 1986, the space shuttle *Challenger* blew up shortly after lift-off, killing all seven on board. In 1989, the supertanker *Exxon Valdez* leaked a gigantic spill of oil into the sea south of Alaska. The oil slick killed millions of seabirds, seals, whales and other marine creatures. Also during this time, another great problem was developing. Scientists had discovered a thinning or lessening in the ozone layer. This is a blanket of the gas ozone (a form of oxgyen) in the upper atmosphere. It helps to absorb some of the Sun's harmful ultra-violet rays. With less ozone, more rays could pass through and reach the surface, possibly harming plant and animal life. For many people, science was to blame for all these tragedies.

Chemical fertilizers and hi-tech farm machines increased crop yields. Yet as surplus grain piled up in rich nations, millions starved in poor regions.

LESS OZONE

The ozone 'layer' is a region of the atmosphere where small amounts of ozone are mixed with the normal gases in the air. Ozone loss or depletion was detected over the South Pole from photos and samples taken by high-flying aircraft in 1987. The loss was traced to certain chemicals such as CFCs used in industrial processes.

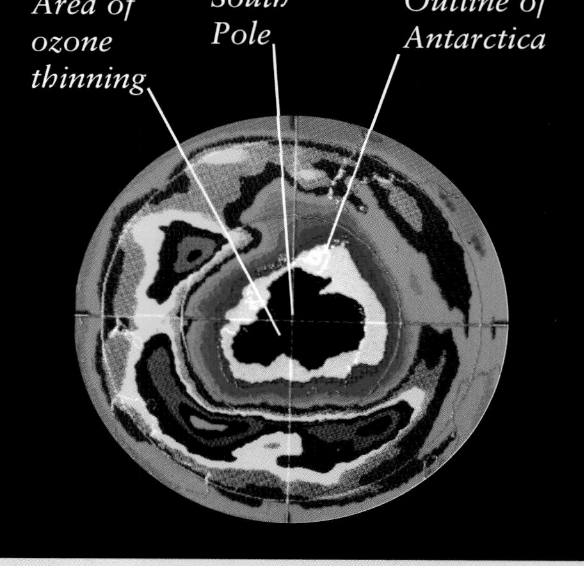

1970-90

ON THE MOVE

Shrinking electronics meant many processes could be made automatic – even flying a jetliner.

RIVALS

In 1970, several European nations grouped together to form Airbus Industries. Their plan was to build large jet passenger aircraft that could rival those of huge US plane manufacturers such as Boeing, Lockheed and McDonnell-Douglas. Their first plane, the Airbus *A300*, made its initial flight in 1972.

The use of industrial robots, ideal in the difficult conditions of a car factory, became widespread in the mid '70s.

The Airbus A340 was given the go-ahead in 1987 and went into service in 1993.

EUROPLANES

Airbus planes are a cooperative effort between many European countries. Different parts such as the wings, fuselage, tail and engines are built in different places, then transported for final assembly at Toulouse, France. The *A340* carries 375 passengers as standard, 260 on very long flights where more fuel is needed, and 440 on short trips.

Spain
Belgium
France
Germany
England

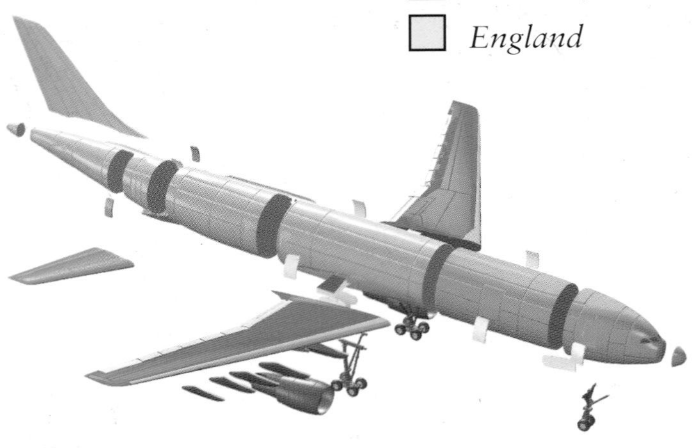

FLY-BY-WIRE

Airbus pioneered the 'fly-by-wire' system. Previously the main controls on the flight deck were linked directly to the aircraft's parts, such as the rudder on the tail fin, by cables or pipes. In fly-by-wire, the plane's computer senses movements of the controls, converts these into electrical signals and sends them along wires to electric motors that work the parts. The computer also monitors other systems and warns the crew of problems.

Australia's Sydney Opera House is designed to look like a ship's sails billowing in the wind – or shells piled up on the sea shore.

NEW MATERIALS

Technologists continued to develop new materials including different types of steels, concretes and carbon fibre composites (see below). The strength, toughness and adaptable nature of these materials allowed designers to create spectacular shapes and effects. A symbol of the time was the Sydney Opera House, opened in 1973. It stands on a narrow strip of land jutting out into Sydney Harbour and has a series of vast curved roofs made of reinforced concrete covered with gleaming white ceramic tiles. In 1981, the Humber Bridge, England set a new record for the longest single bridge span, 1,410 metres.

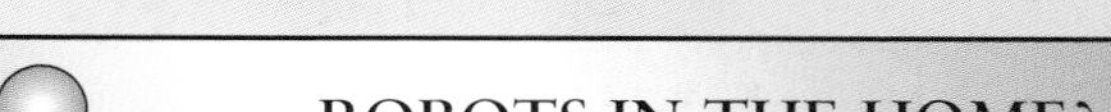

ROBOTS IN THE HOME?

From the 1970s, computer-controlled robot machines appeared on many production lines. After they had been 'taught' by a human, they carried out the same movements precisely, every time, without becoming tired or distracted. However more 'intelligent' robots to help with household chores were still a dream.

A robot waiter clears away dirty dishes – amusing but not very practical!

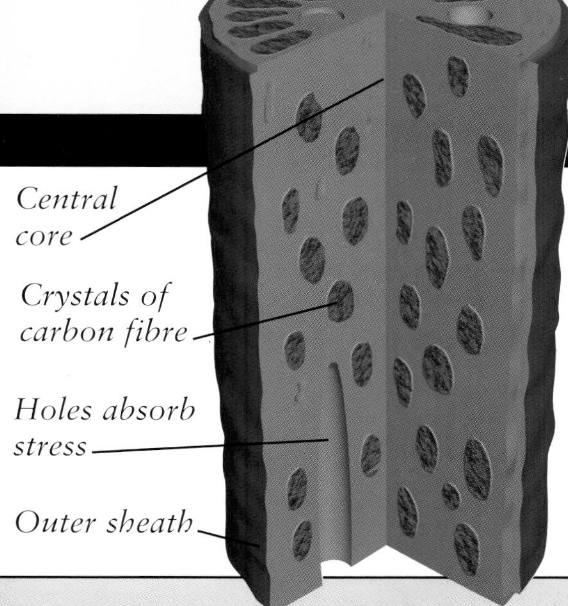

FIBRES, RESINS AND HOLES

Carbon fibre composites are made from fibres of a carbon-based substance, such as artificial rayons or acrylics, and a rubbery, flexible resin-based material. The resulting composite is five times stronger weight for weight than steel, but it bends to absorb stresses rather than cracking.

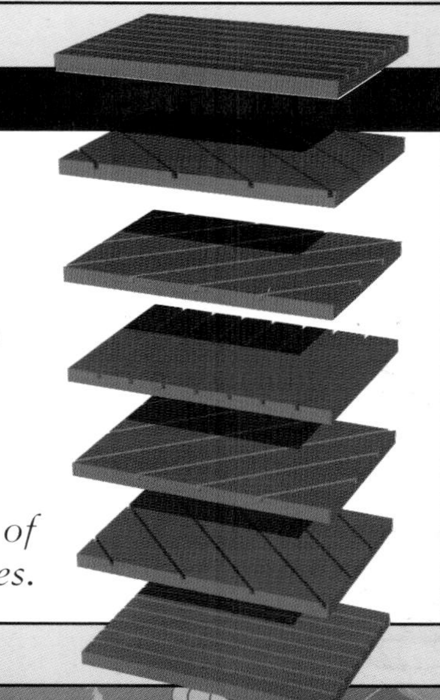

In carbon fibre laminate, layers of fibres are at different angles.

ALTERNATIVE ENERGY

In 1973, world politics and finance were shaken when the oil-producing nations raised oil prices and restricted supplies.

WAVE POWER

Any form of motion represents energy. Could wave energy be harnessed as electricity? Many designs were tried, including Salter's ducks which rock as waves pass. But none has proved practical. Huge storm waves usually damage them.

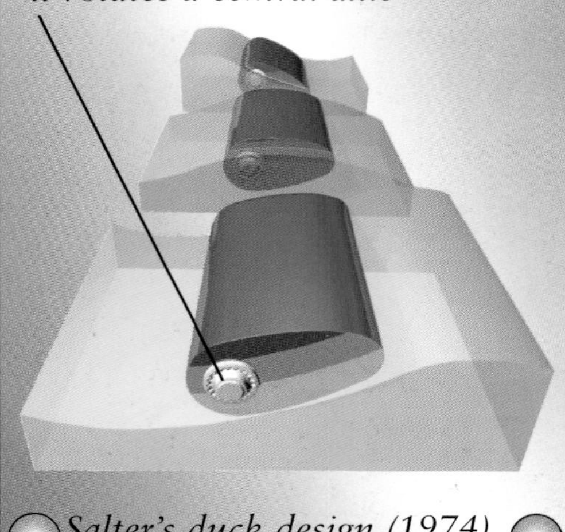

As the duck rocks up and down it rotates a central axle

Salter's duck design (1974).

THE OIL CRISIS

The sudden leap in the price of oil made industrial regions realize how much they depended on this valuable resource. Oil is processed to make fuels, lubricants, plastics, chemicals and hundreds of other products, as well as being burned in power stations. To lessen this dependence, reduce the pollution it causes and make the oil supplies last longer, the search began for other sources of energy.

The Hoover Dam (right) on the Colorado River in Nevada, USA was completed as early as 1936. By 1980, its 17 generators were providing 2,000 megawatts of electricity.

HYDROELECTRICITY

One form of alternative energy that has grown hugely since the 1970s is hydroelectricity. Flowing water spins the angled blades of a turbine which is linked to an electricity generator. Once built, a hydroelectric power station needs no fuel, produces no air pollution and has low maintenance costs. To increase the pressure and flow of water, and to make it more reliable through the year, these power stations are usually sited in dams across large rivers.

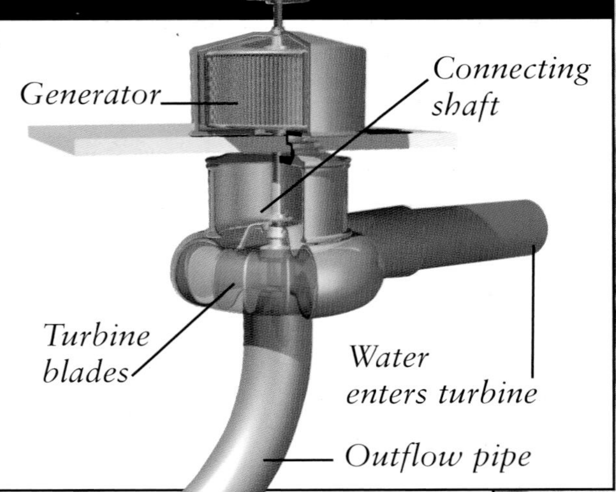

SUN POWER

A 'free' source of energy is the Sun. Its light can be trapped by solar (photovoltaic) cells, small electronic devices laid out together to form larger solar panels. Mainly developed for satellites, solar cells were used more during the '80s. Heat from the Sun can be focused by mirrors on to a central tower and used to generate electricity. This is a solar furnace.

The Barstow Solar Furnace in California, USA was tested in 1982. It has 1,818 mirrors.

WIND POWER

In ancient times wind was used to turn the sails of windmills. A modern version of the windmill appeared in 1982 in Goldendale, Washington, USA. This was a 'wind farm' consisting of many wind turbines or aerogenerators. Wind spins the blades which are linked to an electricity generator. But, like solar power, wind power is only available in certain places and times of the day or year.

Wind farms, such as this one in California, can produce many megawatts of electricity. They successfully channel a natural source of energy, but many people, especially those living near them, consider them to be an eyesore.

COMPUTER

In the industrial world today there is a computer in almost every office and home. But in 1970 computers were big and costly, used only by large businesses, universities and governments.

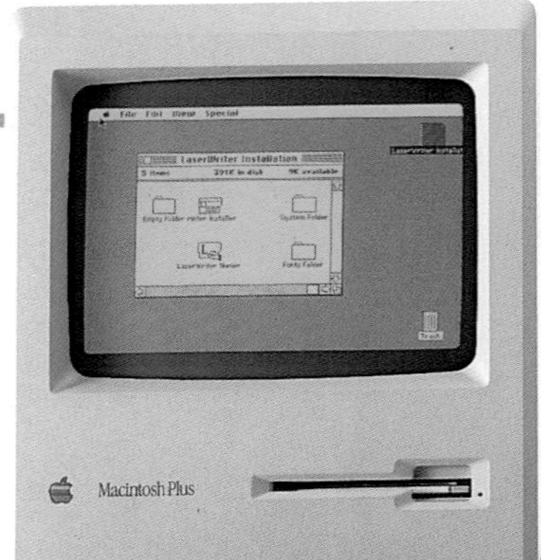

The Apple Macintosh range of small computers began in the 1980s.

COMPUTER PROGRESS

The era of the personal computer, small and cheap enough to buy for home use, began in 1975 with the Altair *8800*. This was advanced for its time but not especially successful. The Apple *II* followed in 1977 and was much more popular. In 1981, IBM introduced its first PC, Personal Computer, with floppy disks and many other features still recognized today.

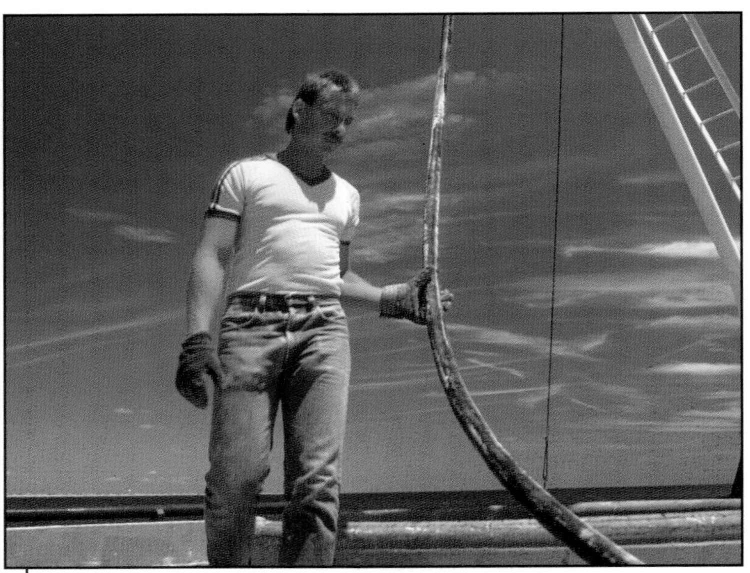

In 1985 a newly developed type of fibre-optic, conveying information as coded flashes of laser light, increased the carrying capacity of one hair-thin fibre to 300,000 telephone calls.

THE COMPUTER SET-UP

The basic personal computer took shape during the late 1970s–early 1980s. Floppy disks had appeared ten years earlier. The Apple *Lisa* of 1983 was the first version with a mouse controlling a pointer on the screen, and a mouse button to click on different choices or options. It also had the 'pull-down menus' or lists so familiar today. PCs have not changed much in size or shape since. But as a rough guide they double in power, memory and processing speed every 18-24 months.

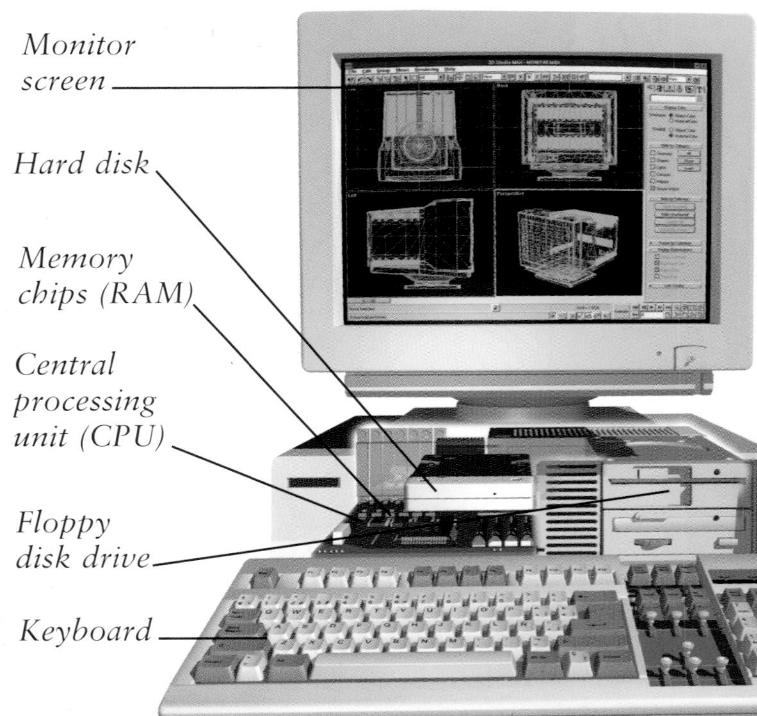

GLOBAL COMMUNICATION

In December 1980, the first of a new generation of satellites was blasted into orbit. It was a comsat (communications satellite) of the International Telecommunications Satellite Organization, *Intelsat V*. More than 100 nations became involved in the organization and 14 more *Intelsat Vs* were launched over the following years. Their main job was to detect radio signals and microwaves coming up from one part of the Earth, boost them to higher strengths, and send them back down to another part of the Earth thousands of kilometres away. The radio and microwave signals represented all kinds of information, in particular telephone calls, television programmes and computer data. The growing comsat network allowed TV programmes to be beamed live to almost every region of the world.

The main body of each Intelsat V *was 6 m long and the solar panels 15 m across. The satellite could carry 12,000 phone calls and two TV channels at the same time.* Intelsats *relayed worldwide TV events such as the Live Aid concert for famine relief in 1985.*

The mouse was a boon to new computer-users. It transfers natural hand movements, as when writing or drawing with a pen, on to the screen. The rubber ball inside rolls as the mouse moves along and spins sensors that track its motion.

Roller sensors pick up movement which is fed to the computer.

Click switch

Rolling ball

1970-90 TRAVEL-TECH

The oil crisis of the 1970s put a global brake on developing bigger, faster types of travel. The focus of research changed to less noise, waste and pollution.

The Anglo-French Concorde *went into service in 1976 after seven years of test flights, more than any other jetliner.*

SLOWDOWN

The supersonic airliner *Concorde*, which could cruise at twice the speed of sound, suffered from the worldwide slowdown. People preferred to take an hour or two extra on their journey but pay much less. Also many cities suffered from massive traffic jams and blankets of smog caused by belching vehicle fumes. So they started to plan RMTs – rapid mass transit systems to carry many people quickly, quietly and safely with minimal waste and pollution. Most systems chose electric railcars or monorails.

A monorail wends through Sydney, Australia. Overhead electric monorails pass above existing streets and are energy-efficient and quiet. In the 1980s they were constructed in many cities, from San Francisco, USA to Beijing, China.

An electric car is about 90 per cent energy-efficient, compared to 25–30 per cent for a petrol-driven car. But this 1984 electric car had so many standard car batteries that it was too heavy and slow.

FALSE START

The Sinclair *C5* (1985) was an attempt at a small, personal electric vehicle for short trips. It was driven by the electric motor from a washing machine! However drivers were unprotected from the weather and felt unsafe, so the *C5* failed.

The battery-powered 3-wheeled Sinclair C5.

AN ATTRACTIVE SOLUTION

A very different form of rail transport was the maglev train, developed from the 1970s in Japan, Germany and Britain. 'Maglev' means magnetic levitation and uses a feature of magnetism. A magnet has two regions of strongest magnetic force called its north and south poles. Like poles, such as north and north, push away or repel each other. Unlike poles, north and south, pull together or attract. Most maglev trains have magnets with one pole facing the track, which has the same pole. The two repel and so the train 'floats' above the track, held up by magnetic force. Various maglevs were tried over the years but a major problem is the cost of the track with so many magnets.

How maglev works

One set of magnets makes the train rise or levitate, which reduces noise and the energy wasted through friction in an ordinary engine and wheels system. The other set switches on and off rapidly to pull or attract the train from the front and repel or push it from behind, so moving the train forwards.

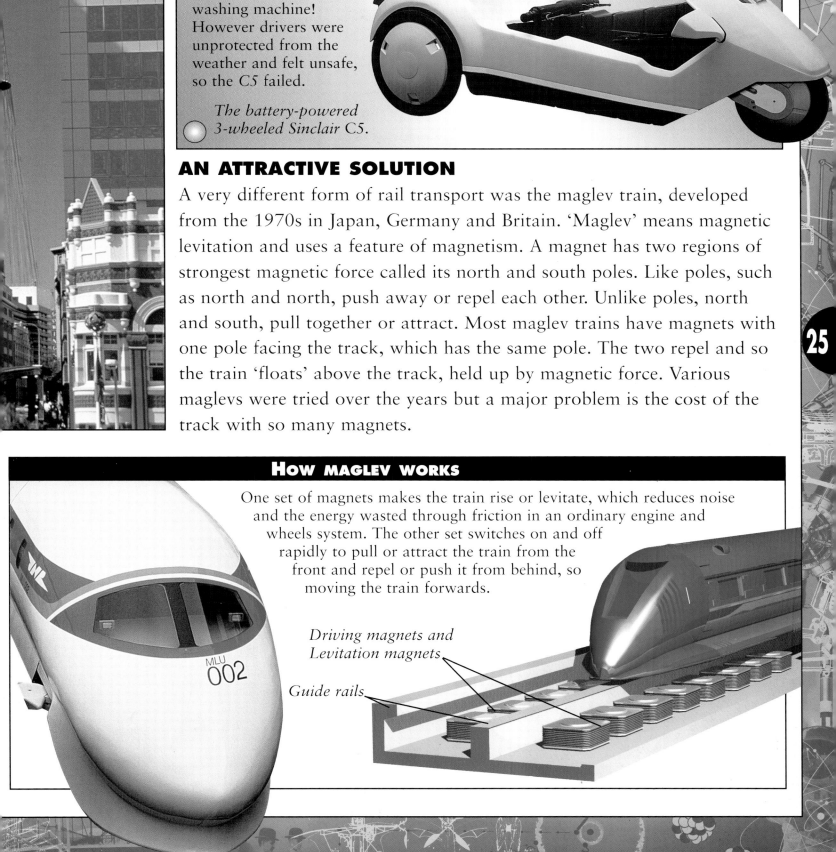

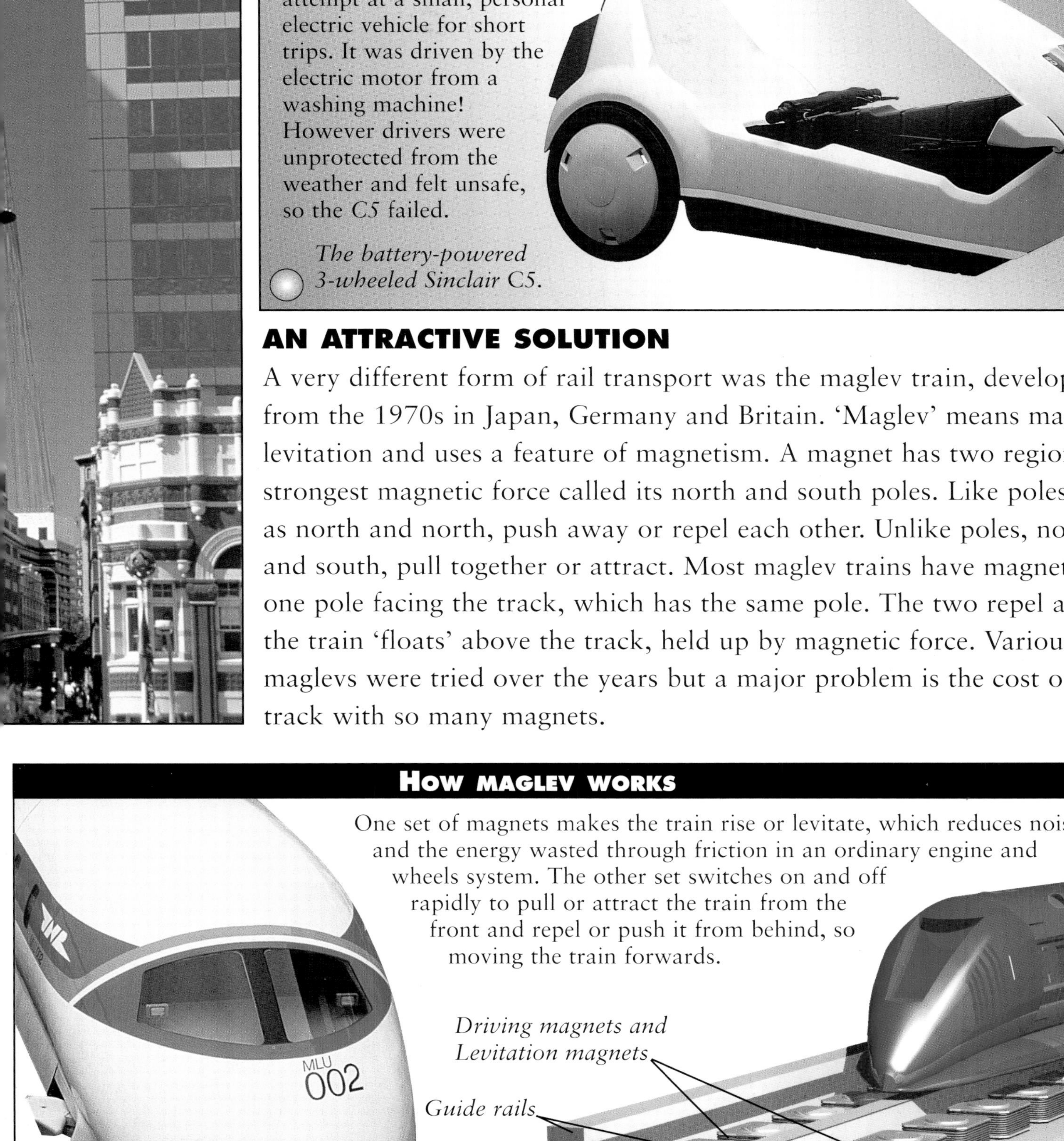

1970-90

MEDICAL SCIENCE

The electronics revolution greatly affected medical technology as a new generation of equipment began to appear in medical centres.

SEEING INTO THE BODY

One of the major advances was in body imaging – seeing inside the body without cutting it open. The CT (computerized tomography) scanner uses very weak X–rays to take pictures of thin 'slices' through the body and combine these into a three-dimensional image. It was developed in 1972. The next year saw the MR (magnetic resonance) scanner. This places the body in a very strong magnetic field and fires tiny radio pulses through it. Both types of scanner relied on the processing power of the new computers.

In the USA, a permanent artificial heart was first put into a human patient, Barney Clark, in 1982. He lived for 112 days.

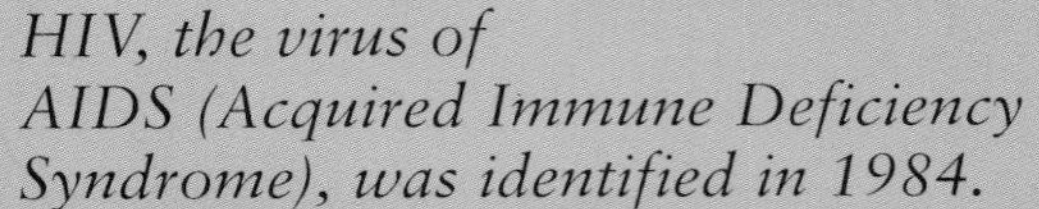

HIV, the virus of AIDS (Acquired Immune Deficiency Syndrome), was identified in 1984.

SEEING THE INVISIBLE

Another leap forward was advanced electron microscopes. These use beams of electrons rather than light rays, to magnify objects a million times or more. One of the objects was HIV, Human Immunodeficiency Virus, which causes the condition of AIDS, which was recognized in about 1981. The year before, the disease of smallpox had been declared wiped out.

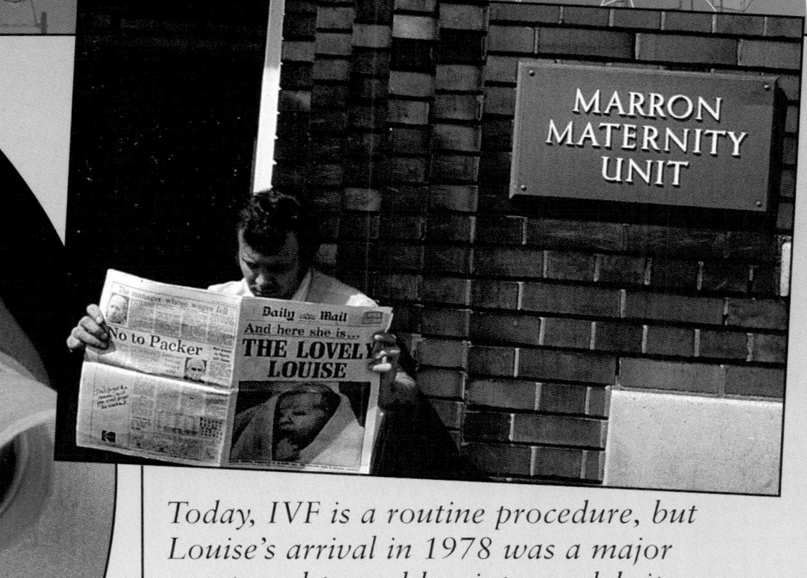

Today, IVF is a routine procedure, but Louise's arrival in 1978 was a major event, and turned her into a celebrity.

TEST TUBE BABIES

The first 'test tube' baby, Louise, was born to mother Lesley Brown in Oldham, England in 1978. Test tubes are not actually used, however. Tiny ripe eggs are obtained from the mother (or a donor) by a rod-like device, the laparoscope, often used for keyhole surgery. The eggs are mixed with sperm from the father (or another donor) in a shallow glass dish. Sperm and egg join or fertilize and begin to develop into an embryo, which is put into the mother's womb to grow into a baby. The method is called IVF, *in vitro* ('in glass') fertilization.

SHATTERING STONES

In 1980 a new type of medical machine was devised to shatter hard, stony lumps that sometimes form inside the body, usually inside the kidneys or gall bladder. The lithotripsy machine fires powerful high-pitched or ultrasonic sound waves at the stone. They make the stone vibrate and break into many tiny pieces which can pass out of the body naturally.

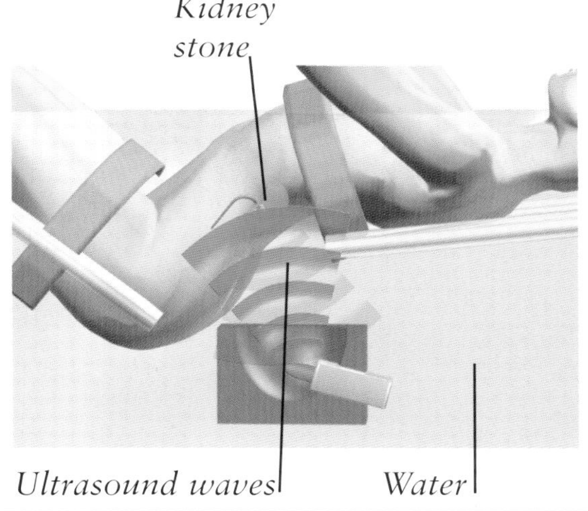

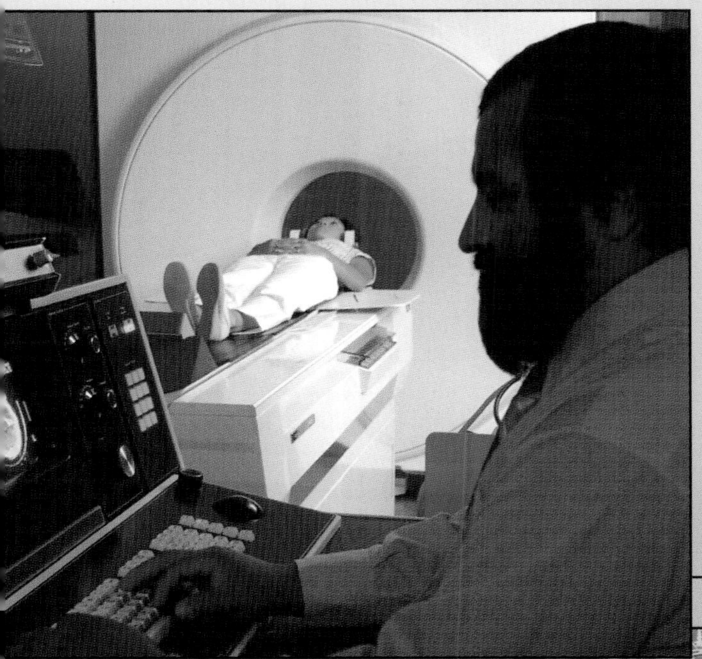

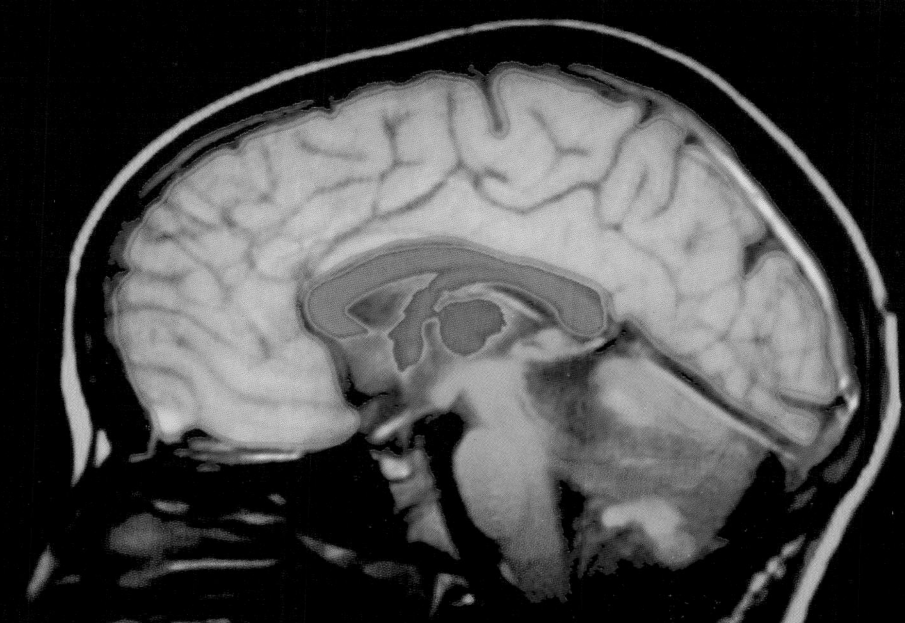

The MR scanner (left) gives doctors clear and detailed pictures, with the added bonus of not using X-rays.

MR and CT scans are often coloured by computer to show parts more clearly. The yellow here is the brain's cortex or 'thinking part'.

GADGETS

The gadget revolution that began in the 1970s was based on electronic integrated circuits (ICs) – known as silicon chips, microchips or simply 'chips'.

As microchips advanced in processing speed they could control increasingly more complex and fast-moving video games.

CHIPS EVERYWHERE

A microchip is a small sliver or wafer of the substance silicon, just a few millimetres square, with lots of microscopic lines, patterns and shapes on its surface. Silicon is a semiconductor. Under some conditions it carries or conducts electricity well, in other conditions it does not. The items on the chip use this feature to work as resistors, transistors and other electronic components. They make circuits that alter and manipulate pulses of electricity at incredible speed.

ON THE MOVE

When a microchip is made the components are already connected or integrated into circuits, rather than linked later by wires, giving the term IC. Chips are tiny, light, tough and use very little electricity so they only need small batteries. This makes them ideal for portable electronic gadgets.

The Sony Walkman personal stereo radio-cassette player (1979) was a vital 'bit of kit' for the new, fast, on-the move lifestyle. It also played music!

The stick-on, peel-off note of 1980 turned a 'failed' glue, too weak for ordinary use, into a massive success.

WORK AND PLAY

Some of these small, lightweight gadgets were mainly for work, such as speech recorders and pocket calculators. Others were for entertainment, like personal music players and hand-held games consoles. Another vital part of the gadget revolution was the LCD, liquid crystal display. It shows patterns of dark shapes on a clear background according to the electronic signals it receives. Like the IC it is tiny, tough and uses very little electricity.

Mobile phones had begun to appear by the end of the 1980s, although they were expensive and bulky compared to today's versions. They were mainly for business use.

THE LCD

An LCD is a sandwich of units including polarizing filters (as in polarizing sunglasses). The crystal part can twist the light rays so that they do not pass through the filter or reflect off the mirror at the base, making a dark area.

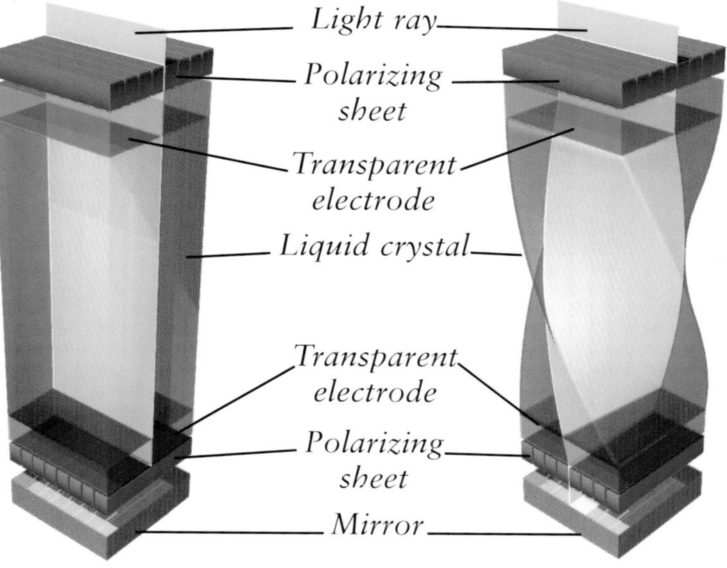

Nintendo's Game Boy (1989) had five microchips. Its LCD screen showed small, simple moving pictures. It sold 100 million in four years.

GLOSSARY

AEROGENERATOR A modern version of the windmill, with large angled blades on a tall tower, which converts wind power into electricity. Also called a wind turbine.

ATOM The smallest part of a pure substance (chemical element) that can exist naturally. Most atoms are made of three types of even tinier particles called protons, neutrons and electrons.

BLACK HOLE A place where space and time curve in an infinite way, so matter is concentrated into an unimaginably small space yet has incredibly huge gravitational attraction.

COMPOSITE A structural or engineering material made from various substances or ingredients, including metals, ceramics and carbon-based fibres, to combine the desired properties of each.

DEEP-SEA HYDROTHERMAL VENT A hole or crack in the bottom of the sea, where hot mineral-rich water and gases spurt and bubble up from far below.

ELECTROMAGNETIC SPECTRUM A whole range or spectrum of waves consisting of combined electrical and magnetic energy. They include radio and TV waves, microwaves, infra-red, light rays, ultra-violet, X-rays and gamma rays.

METEOROLOGY The study of Earth's atmosphere, especially clouds and winds, weather and climate.

NUCLEAR REACTOR The main part of a nuclear power unit, where a chain reaction occurs as nuclei (central parts of atoms) of the atomic fuel split and release huge amounts of heat and other forms of energy.

OZONE A form of the chemical element oxygen, but with three oxygen atoms joined to form each molecule, O_3, rather than two as in normal oxygen gas molecule, O_2.

PAYLOAD The items or cargo carried by a plane, ship, spaceship or other craft, rather than being parts of the actual craft itself.

SOLID ROCKET BOOSTER A rocket that uses solid fuel, in pellets, rather than the usual liquid fuel, and which is added on to another spacecraft to boost or increase its speed, especially at launch.

WORLD EVENTS

- *Manila: assassination attempt on Pope Paul* 1
- *Idi Amin seizes power in Uganda* 1
- *Britain: Strikes, 3-Day Week and power cuts* 1
- *Ceasefire in Vietnam* / *Oil crisis, prices rocket* 1
- *US President Nixon, Watergate scandal* 1
- *Khmer Rouge seize power in Cambodia* 1
- *China: Mao Tse-Tung, revolutionary leader, dies* 1
- *General Zia seizes power in Pakistan* 1
- *Shi-ite Muslim uprising against the Shah in Iran* 1
- *Russia quells civil war in Afghanistan* 1
- *Poland: Solidarity trade unions begin* 1
- *Ronald Reagan become US President* 1
- *Argentina invades British Falkland Islands* 1
- *Suicide bombers kill hundreds in Lebanon* 1
- *Massive famine in Ethiopia, millions die* 1
- *Mikhail Gorbachev takes power in USSR* 1
- *USSR begins to loosen communist controls* 1
- *Tamil freedom fighters bombed in Sri Lanka* 1
- *Iran-Iraq ceasefire after terrible bloodshed* 1
- *Tiananmen Square massacre in China* 1

TIMELINE

	SCIENCE EVENTS	TECHNOLOGY	FAMOUS SCIENTISTS	INVENTIONS
70	•Apollo 13 mission cut short, crew saved	•Carbon dioxide lasers for cutting and welding	•Stephen Cook shows many logic problems are one	•Removeable floppy computer disc
71	•First microprocessors, tiny electronic 'brains'	•First long-term space station, USSR's Salyut 1	•Niklaus Wirth's PASCAL computer language	•'Pocket' calculator •Food processor
72	•Massive new atom-smasher, Batavia, USA	•BBC's Ceefax system for television information	•Murray Gell-Mann links quantum theory and quarks	•Home video game, the bat-and-ball 'Odyssey'
73	•Skylab launched •Pioneer 10 at Jupiter	•First tuneable continuous pulse laser	•E Tryon suggests Universe could start from nothing	•Push-in rather than pull-off ring-tabs for drink cans
74	•Signs of ozone damage become clearer	•Early design for wave power device (Salter's duck)	•Don Johanson and team find ancient 'Lucy' fossils	•Bar code laser scanners used in retail stores
75	•European Space Agency formed	•First LCDs, liquid crystal displays	•John Cornforth's Nobel Prize for work on enzymes	•First home computer available in kit form
76	•Guidelines agreed for genetic engineering	•Supersonic jetliner Concorde in regular service	•Khorana and team make an artificial gene	•Ink-jet printer •Fibre-optic telecom cables
77	•Last natural case of smallpox, Somalia	•Gossamer Condor *human-powered aircraft*	•Efron's 'bootstrap' high-speed computer statistics	•Mass-produced pocket TV with 5-cm screen
78	•Electron beams make microchips even smaller	•Apple disc drive for small computers	•Christy and Harrington find Pluto's moon, Charon	•Jobs and Wozniak's Apple II home computer
79	•Three Mile Island nuclear accident, USA	•Computer spreadsheets •Vehicle exhaust CATs	•Jean Ichbia develops ADA computer language	•Walkman personal stereo •Videocassettes widespread
80	•Scientists record Mt St Helens volcanic eruption	•Scanning tunnelling microscope sees one atom	•Alan Guth suggests inflationary Universe idea	•Erno Rubik's cube sparks puzzle craze
81	•First space shuttle and stealth fighter flights	•Electronic video camera (no tape or film)	•Fukui and Hoffman Nobel Prize for quantum chemistry	•IBM Personal Computer, PC, with MS-DOS
82	•Agreement to curb ozone-damaging CFCs	•Goldendale wind farm, US, generates electricity	•Mike Freedman's maths for four-dimensional space	•CDs appear •First PC computer 'clone'
83	•Global warming, acid rain are world news	•IRAS heat-detecting satellite	•Walther Ghering discovers 'homeobox' gene in worms	•Satellite TV direct to homes, Indianapolis, US
84	•AIDS virus, HIV, identified	•Detection of 'top' quark, the heaviest one	•Alec Jeffreys develops genetic fingerprinting	•Camcorder for video 'home movies'
85	•US 'Star Wars' space defence plan	•Cosmic string theory begins to take off	•Clive Sinclair's C5 battery tricycle-car – fails	•Desktop publishing, Apple and other computers
86	•Challenger shuttle and Chernobyl disasters	•Voyager 2 finds 10 more moons of Uranus	• Rutan and Yeager's non-stop round-the world flight	•Lasers treat clogged arteries in the heart
87	•Genetic engineering: fast-growing 'superfish'	•Gene gun fires genetic material into living cells	•Madrazo's new treatment for Parkinson's disease	•DAT, digital audio tape •4-wheel drive on many cars
88	•First planets detected outside Solar System	•Colour laser photocopier developed	•Stephen Hawking's book, A Brief History of Time	•Cellular (mobile) phones begin to appear
89	•'Cold fusion' claims could not be supported	•Voyager 2 reaches Neptune	•Robert Morris jailed in US for computer virus crime	•Gameboy pocket video game

INDEX